Best in Children's Books

Copyright ©, 1959, by Nelson Doubleday, Inc.
Garden City, New York   26

The Wild Swans

by HANS CHRISTIAN ANDERSEN

illustrated by COLLEEN BROWNING

Text from *Hans Andersen's Fairy Tales*, translated by Mrs. Edgar Lucas.
Children's Illustrated Classics. Reprinted by permission of the publishers,
E. P. Dutton & Company, Inc.

Far away, where the swallows take refuge in winter, lived a king who had eleven sons and one daughter, Elise. The eleven brothers—they were all princes—used to go to school with stars on their breasts and swords at their sides. They wrote upon golden slates with diamond pencils, and could read just as well without a book as with one, so there was no mistake about their being real princes. Their sister Elise sat upon a little footstool of looking glass, and she had a picture book which had cost the half of a kingdom. Oh, these children were very happy; but it was not to last thus forever.

Their father, who was king over all the land, married a wicked queen, who was not at all kind to the poor children; they found that out on the first day. All was festive at the castle, but when the children wanted to play at having company, instead of having as many cakes and baked apples as ever they wanted, she would only let them have some sand in a teacup, and said they must make believe.

In the following week she sent little Elise into the country to board with some peasants, and it did not take her long to make the king believe so many bad things about the boys, that he cared no more about them.

"Fly out into the world and look after yourselves," said the wicked queen. "You shall fly about like birds without voices."

But she could not make things as bad for them as she would have liked; they turned into eleven beautiful wild swans. They flew out of the palace window with a weird scream, right across the park and the woods.

It was very early in the morning when they came to the place where their sister Elise was sleeping in the peasants' house. They hovered over the roof of the house, turning and twisting their long necks, and flapping their wings; but no one either heard or saw them. They had to fly away again, and they soared up towards the clouds, far out into the wide world, and they settled in a big, dark wood, which stretched down to the shore.

Poor little Elise stood in the peasants' room, playing with a green leaf, for she had no other toys. She made a little hole in it, which she looked through at the sun, and it seemed to her as if she saw her brothers' bright eyes. Every time the warm sunbeams shone upon her cheek it reminded her of their kisses. One day passed just like another. When the wind whistled through the rose hedges outside the house it whispered to the roses: "Who can be prettier than you are?" But the roses shook their heads and answered, "Elise!" And when the old woman sat in the doorway reading her psalms, the wind turned over the leaves and said to the book: "Who can be more pious than you?"

5

"Elise!" answered the book. Both the roses and the book of psalms only spoke the truth.

She was to go home when she was fifteen; but when the queen saw how pretty she was she got very angry, and her heart was filled with hatred. She would willingly have turned her into a wild swan too, like her brothers, but she did not dare to do it at once, for the king wanted to see his daughter. The queen always went to the bath in the early morning. It was built of marble and adorned with soft cushions and beautiful carpets.

She took three toads, kissed them, and said to the first: "Sit upon Elise's head when she comes to the bath, so that she may become sluggish like yourself. Sit upon her forehead," she said to the second, "that she may become ugly like you, and then her father won't know her! Rest upon her heart," she whispered to the third. "Let an evil spirit come over her, which may be a burden to her." Then she put the toads into the clean water, and a green tinge immediately came over it. She called Elise, undressed her, and made her go into the bath; when she ducked under the water, one of the toads got among her hair, the other got onto her forehead, and the third onto her bosom. But when she stood up three scarlet poppies floated on the water; had

not the creatures been poisonous, and kissed by the sorceress, they would have been changed into crimson roses, but yet they became flowers from merely having rested a moment on her head and her heart. She was far too good and innocent for the sorcery to have any power over her. When the wicked queen saw this she rubbed her over with walnut juice, and smeared her face with some evil-smelling salve. She also matted up her beautiful hair; it would have been impossible to recognize pretty Elise. When her father saw her he was quite horrified and said that she could not be his daughter. Nobody would have anything to say to her, except the yard dog and the swallows, and they were only poor dumb animals whose opinion went for nothing.

Poor Elise wept, and thought of her eleven brothers who were all lost. She crept sadly out of the palace and wandered about all day, over meadows and marshes, and into a big forest. She did not know in the least where she wanted to go, but she felt very sad, and longed for her brothers, who, no doubt, like herself had been driven out of the palace. She made up her mind to go and look for them, but she had only been in the wood for a short time when night fell. She had quite lost her way, so she lay down upon the soft moss, said her evening prayer, and rested her head on a little hillock. It was very still and the air was

mild; hundreds of glowworms shone around her on the grass and in the marsh like green fire. When she gently moved one of the branches over her head, the little shining insects fell over her like a shower of stars. She dreamt about her brothers all night long. Again they were children playing together: they wrote upon the golden slates with their diamond pencils, and she looked at the picture book which had cost half a kingdom. But they no longer wrote strokes and noughts upon their slates as they used to do; no, they wrote down all their boldest exploits and everything that they had seen and experienced. Everything in the picture book was alive; the birds sang, and the people walked out of the book and spoke to Elise and her brothers. When she turned over a page they skipped back into their places again, so that there should be no confusion among the pictures.

When she woke the sun was already high; it is true she could not see it very well through the thick branches of the lofty forest trees, but the sunbeams cast a golden shimmer around beyond the forest. There was a fresh delicious scent of grass and herbs in the air, and the birds were almost ready to perch upon her shoulders. She could hear the splashing of water, for there were many springs around, which all flowed into a pond with a lovely sandy bottom. It was surrounded with thick bushes, but there was one place which the stags had trampled down and Elise passed through the opening to the waterside. It was so transparent that had not the branches been moved by the breeze she must have thought that they were painted on the bottom, so plainly was every leaf reflected, both those on which the sun played and those which were in shade.

When she saw her own face she was quite frightened, it was so brown and ugly, but when she wet her little hand and rubbed her eyes and forehead, her white skin shone through again. Then she took off all her clothes and went into the fresh water. A more beautiful royal child than she could not be found in all the world.

When she had put on her clothes again, and plaited her long hair, she went to a sparkling spring and drank some of the water out of the hollow of her hand. Then she wandered further into the wood, though where she was going she had not the least idea. She thought of her brothers, and she thought of a merciful God who would not forsake her. He let the wild crab apples grow to feed the hungry. He showed her a tree, the branches of which were bending beneath their weight of fruit. Here she made her midday meal, and, having put props under the branches, she walked on into the thickest part of the forest. It was so quiet that she heard her own footsteps; she heard every little withered leaf which bent under her feet. Not a bird was to be seen, not a ray of sunlight pierced the leafy branches, and the tall trunks were so close together that when she looked before her it seemed as if a thick fence of heavy beams hemmed her in on every side. The solitude was such as she had never known before.

It was a very dark night; not a single glowworm sparkled in the marsh. Sadly she lay down to sleep; and it seemed to her as if the branches above her parted asunder, and the Saviour looked down upon her with His loving eyes, and little angels' heads peeped out above His head and under His arms.

When she woke in the morning she was not sure if she had dreamt this, or whether it was really true.

She walked a little further, when she met an old woman with a basket full of berries, of which she gave her some. Elise asked if she had seen eleven princes ride through the wood. "No," said the old woman, "but yesterday I saw eleven swans, with golden crowns upon their heads, swimming in the stream close by there."

She led Elise a little further to a slope, at the foot of which the stream meandered. The trees on either bank stretched out their rich leafy branches towards each other, and where, from their natural growth, they could not reach each other, they had torn their roots out of the ground, and leant over the water so as to interlace their branches.

Elise said good-by to the old woman, and walked along by the river till it flowed out into the great open sea.

The beautiful open sea lay before the maiden, but not a sail was to be seen on it, not a single boat. How was she ever to get any further? She looked at the numberless little pebbles on the beach; they were all worn quite round by the water. Glass, iron, stone, whatever was washed up, had taken their shapes from the water, which yet was much softer than her little hand. "With all its rolling, it is untiring, and everything hard is smoothed down. I will be just as untiring! Thank you for your lesson, you clear rolling waves! Sometime, so my heart tells me, you will bear me to my beloved brothers!"

Eleven white swans' feathers were lying on the seaweed; she picked them up and made a bunch of them. There were still drops of water on them. Whether these were dew or

tears no one could tell. It was very lonely there by the
shore, but she did not feel it, for the sea was ever changing.
There were more changes on it in the course of a few hours
than could be seen on an inland fresh-water lake in a year.

15

If a big black cloud arose it was just as if the sea wanted to say, "I can look black too," and then the wind blew up and the waves showed their white crests. But if the clouds were red and the wind dropped, the sea looked like a rose leaf, now white, now green. But, however still it was, there was always a little gentle motion just by the shore; the water rose and fell softly like the bosom of a sleeping child.

When the sun was just about to go down Elise saw eleven wild swans with golden crowns upon their heads flying towards the shore. They flew in a swaying line, one behind the other, like a white ribbon streamer. Elise climbed up onto the bank and hid behind a bush; the swans settled close by her and flapped their great white wings.

As soon as the sun had sunk beneath the water the swans shed their feathers and became eleven handsome princes; they were Elise's brothers. Although they had altered a good deal she knew them at once; she felt that they must be her brothers and she sprang into their arms, calling them by name. They were delighted when they recognized their little sister who had grown so big and beautiful. They

laughed and cried, and told each other how wickedly their stepmother had treated them all.

"We brothers," said the eldest, "have to fly about in the guise of swans, as long as the sun is above the horizon. When it goes down we regain our human shapes. So we always have to look out for a resting place near sunset, for should we happen to be flying up among the clouds when the sun goes down, we should be hurled to the depths below. We do not live here; there is another land, just as beautiful as this, beyond the sea; but the way to it is very long, and we have to cross the mighty ocean to get to it. There is not a single island on the way where we can spend the night; only one solitary little rock juts up above the water midway. It is only just big enough for us to stand upon close together, and if there is a heavy sea the water splashes over us, yet we thank our God for it. We stay there overnight in our human forms, and without it we could never revisit our beloved fatherland, for our flight takes two of the longest days in the year. We are only permitted to visit the home of our fathers once a year, and we dare only stay for eleven days. We hover over this big forest from whence we catch a glimpse of the palace where we were born, and where our father lives; beyond it we can see the high church towers where our mother is buried. We fancy that the trees and bushes here are related to us; and the wild horses gallop over the moors, as we used to see them in our childhood. The charcoal burners still sing the old songs we used to dance to when we were children. This is our fatherland, we are drawn towards it, and here we have found you again, dear little sister! We may stay here two days longer, and then we must fly away again across the ocean, to a lovely country indeed, but it is not our own dear fatherland! How shall we ever take you with us? We have neither ship nor boat!"

"How can I deliver you?" said their sister, and they went on talking to each other nearly all night; they only dozed for a few hours.

Elise was awakened in the morning by the rustling of the swans' wings above her; her brothers were again transformed and were wheeling round in great circles, till she lost sight of them in the distance. One of them, the youngest, stayed behind. He laid his head against her bosom, and she caressed it with her fingers. They remained together all day; towards evening the others came back, and as soon as the sun went down they took their natural forms.

"Tomorrow we must fly away, and we dare not come back for a whole year, but we can't leave you like this! Have you courage to go with us? My arm is strong enough to carry you over the forest, so surely our united strength ought to be sufficient to bear you across the ocean."

"Oh, yes, take me with you!" said Elise.

They spent the whole night in weaving a kind of net of the elastic bark of the willow bound together with tough rushes; they made it both large and strong. Elise lay down upon it, and when the sun rose and the brothers became swans again, they took up the net in their bills and flew high up among the clouds with their precious sister, who was fast asleep. The sunbeams fell straight onto her face, so one of the swans flew over her head so that its broad wings should shade her.

They were far from land when Elise woke; she thought she must still be dreaming, it seemed so strange to be carried through the air so high up above the sea. By her side lay a branch of beautiful ripe berries, and a bundle of savoury roots, which her youngest brother had collected for her, and for which she gave him a grateful smile. She knew it was he who flew above her head shading her from the sun. They were so high up that the first ship they saw looked like a gull floating on the water. A great cloud came up behind them like a mountain, and Elise saw the shadow of herself on it, and those of the eleven swans looking like giants. It was a more beautiful picture than any she had ever seen before, but as the sun rose higher the cloud fell behind, and the shadow picture disappeared.

They flew on and on all day like an arrow whizzing through the air, but they went slower than usual, for now they had their sister to carry. A storm came up, and night was drawing on; Elise saw the sun sinking with terror in

her heart, for the solitary rock was nowhere to be seen. The swans seemed to be taking stronger strokes than ever; alas! she was the cause of their not being able to get on faster; as soon as the sun went down they would become men, and they would all be hurled into the sea and drowned. She prayed to God from the bottom of her heart, but still no rock was to be seen! Black clouds gathered, and strong gusts of wind announced a storm; the clouds looked like a great threatening leaden wave, and the flashes of lightning followed each other rapidly.

The sun was now at the edge of the sea. Elise's heart quaked, when suddenly the swans shot downwards so suddenly that she thought they were falling; then they hovered again. Half of the sun was below the horizon, and there for the first time she saw the little rock below, which did not look bigger than the head of a seal above the water. The sun sank very quickly—it was no bigger than a star—but her foot touched solid earth. The sun went out like the last sparks of a bit of burning paper; she saw her brothers stand arm in arm around her, but there was only just room enough for them. The waves beat upon the rock, and washed over them like drenching rain. The heavens shone with continuous fire, and the thunder rolled, peal upon peal. But the sister and brothers held each other's hands and sang a psalm which gave them comfort and courage.

The air was pure and still at dawn. As soon as the sun rose the swans flew off with Elise, away from the islet. The sea still ran high; it looked from where they were as if the white foam on the dark green water were millions of swans floating on the waves.

When the sun rose higher Elise saw before her, half floating in the air, great masses of ice with shining glaciers on the heights. A palace was perched midway, a mile in length, with one bold colonnade built above another. Beneath them swayed palm trees and gorgeous blossoms as big as mill wheels. She asked if this was the land to which she was going, but the swans shook their heads, because what she saw was a mirage: the beautiful and ever-changing palace of Fata Morgana. No mortal dared enter it. Elise gazed at it, but as she gazed the palace, gardens, and mountains melted away, and in their place stood twenty proud churches with their high towers and pointed windows. She seemed to hear the notes of the organ, but it was the sea she heard. When she got close to the seeming churches they changed to a great navy sailing beneath her; but it was only a sea mist floating over the waters. Yes, she saw constant changes passing before her eyes, and now she saw the real land she was bound to. Beautiful blue mountains rose before her with their cedar woods and palaces. Long before the sun went down she sat among the hills in front of a big cave covered with delicate green creepers. It looked like a piece of embroidery.

"Now we shall see what you will dream here tonight," said the youngest brother, as he showed her where she was to sleep.

"If only I might dream how I could deliver you," she said, and this thought filled her mind entirely. She prayed earnestly to God for His help, and even in her sleep she continued her prayer. It seemed to her that she was flying up to Fata Morgana in her castle in the air. The fairy came towards her; she was charming and brilliant, and yet she was very like the old woman who gave her the berries in the wood, and told her about the swans with the golden crowns.

"Your brothers can be delivered," she said, "but have you courage and endurance enough for it? The sea is indeed softer than your hands, and it moulds the hardest stones, but it does not feel the pain your fingers will feel. It has no heart, and does not suffer the pain and anguish you must feel. Do you see this stinging nettle I hold in my hand? Many of this kind grow round the cave where you sleep; only these and the ones which grow in the churchyards may be used. Mark that! Those you may pluck, although they will burn and blister your hands. Crush the nettles with your feet and you will have flax, and of this you must weave eleven coats of mail with long sleeves. Throw these over the eleven wild swans and the charm is broken! But remember that from the moment you begin this work, till it is finished, even if it takes years, you must

23

not utter a word! The first word you say will fall like a murderer's dagger into the hearts of your brothers. Their lives hang on your tongue. Mark this well!"

She touched Elise's hand at the same moment; it was like burning fire and woke the girl. It was bright daylight, and close to where she slept lay a nettle like those in her

dream. She fell upon her knees with thanks to God and left the cave to begin her work.

She seized the horrid nettles with her delicate hands and they burnt like fire; great blisters rose on her hands and arms, but she suffered it willingly if only it would deliver her beloved brothers. She crushed every nettle with her

25

bare feet, and twisted it into green flax.

When the sun went down and the brothers came back they were alarmed at finding her mute; they thought it was some new witchcraft exercised by their wicked stepmother. But when they saw her hands they understood that it was for their sakes; the youngest brother wept, and wherever his tears fell she felt no more pain and the blisters disappeared.

She spent the whole night at her work, for she could not rest till she had delivered her dear brothers. All the following day while her brothers were away she sat solitary, but never had the time flown so fast. One coat of mail was finished and she began the next. Then a hunting horn sounded among the mountains; she was much frightened, the sound came nearer, and she heard dogs barking. In terror she rushed into the cave and tied the nettles she had collected and woven into a bundle upon which she sat.

At this moment a big dog bounded forward from the thicket, and another and another; they barked loudly and ran backwards and forwards. In a few minutes all the huntsmen were standing outside the cave, and the handsomest of them was the king of the country. He stepped up to Elise: never had he seen so lovely a girl.

"How came you here, beautiful child?" he said.

Elise shook her head; she dared not speak; the salvation and the lives of her brothers depended upon her silence. She hid her hands under her apron, so that the king should not see what she suffered.

"Come with me!" he said. "You cannot stay here. If you are as good as you are beautiful I will dress you in silks and

velvets, put a golden crown upon your head, and you shall
live with me and have your home in my richest palace!"
Then he lifted her upon his horse. She wept and wrung
her hands; but the king said, "I only think of your happi-
ness; you will thank me one day for what I am doing!"
Then he darted off across the mountains, holding her before
him on his horse, and the huntsmen followed.

When the sun went down the royal city with churches
and cupolas lay before them, and the king led her into the
palace, where great fountains played in the marble halls,
and where walls and ceilings were adorned with paintings,
but she had no eyes for them, she only wept and sorrowed;

passively she allowed the women to dress her in royal robes, to twist pearls into her hair, and to draw gloves onto her blistered hands.

She was dazzlingly lovely as she stood there in all her magnificence; the courtiers bent low before her, and the king wooed her as his bride, although the archbishop shook his head, and whispered that he feared the beautiful wood maiden was a witch, who had dazzled their eyes and infatuated the king.

The king refused to listen to him; he ordered the music to play, the richest food to be brought, and the loveliest girls to dance before her. She was led through scented gardens into gorgeous apartments, but nothing brought a smile to her lips or into her eyes; sorrow sat there like a heritage and a possession for all time. Last of all the king opened the door of a little chamber close by the room where she was to sleep. It was adorned with costly green carpets, and made to resemble exactly the cave where he found her. On the floor lay a bundle of flax she had spun from the nettles, and from the ceiling hung the shirt of mail which was already finished. One of the huntsmen had brought all these things away as curiosities.

"Here you may dream that you are back in your former home!" said the king. "Here is the work upon which you were engaged; in the midst of your splendour it may amuse you to think of those times."

When Elise saw all these things so dear to her heart a smile for the first time played upon her lips, and the blood rushed back to her cheeks. She thought of the deliverance of her brothers and she kissed the king's hand; he pressed

her to his heart and ordered all the church bells to ring marriage peals. The lovely dumb girl from the woods was to be queen of the country.

The archbishop whispered evil words into the ear of the king, but they did not reach his heart. The wedding was to take place, and the archbishop himself had to put the crown upon her head. In his anger he pressed the golden circlet so tightly upon her head as to give her pain. But a heavier circlet pressed upon her heart, her grief for her brothers, so she thought nothing of the bodily pain. Her lips were sealed—a single word from her mouth would cost her brothers their lives—but her eyes were full of love for the good and handsome king, who did everything he could to

30

please her. Every day she grew more and more attached to
him, and longed to confide in him, tell him her sufferings;
but dumb she must remain, and in silence must bring her la-
bour to completion. Therefore at night she stole away from
his side into her secret chamber, which was decorated like
a cave, and here she knitted one shirt after another. When
she came to the seventh all her flax was worked up; she
knew that these nettles which she was to use grew in the
churchyard, but she had to pluck them herself. How was
she to get there? "Oh, what is the pain of my fingers com-
pared with the anguish of my heart," she thought. "I must
venture out—the good God will not desert me!" With as
much terror in her heart as if she were doing some evil

deed, she stole down one night into the moonlit garden and through the long alleys out into the silent streets to the churchyard. There she saw, sitting on a gravestone, a group of hideous ghouls. Elise had to pass close by them, and they fixed their evil eyes upon her, but she said a prayer as she passed, picked the stinging nettles, and hurried back to the palace with them.

Only one person saw her, but that was the archbishop, who watched while others slept. Surely now all his bad opinions of the queen were justified; all was not as it should be with her. She must be a witch, and therefore she had be-witched the king and all the people.

He told the king in the confessional what he had seen and what he feared. When those bad words passed his lips the pictures of the saints shook their heads as if to say: "It is not so—Elise is innocent." The archbishop, how-ever, took it differently, and thought that they were bearing witness against her, and shaking their heads at her sin. Two big tears rolled down the king's cheeks, and he went home with doubt in his heart. He pretended to sleep at night, but no quiet sleep came to his eyes. He perceived how Elise got up and went to her private closet. Day by day his face grew darker; Elise saw it but could not imagine what was the cause of it. It alarmed her, and what was she not already suffering in her heart because of her brothers? Her salt tears ran down upon the royal purple velvet; they lay upon it like sparkling diamonds, and all who saw their splendour wished to be queen.

She had, however, almost reached the end of her labours; only one shirt of mail was wanting, but again she had no more flax and not a single nettle was left. Once more, for the last time, she must go to the churchyard to pluck a few handfuls. She thought with dread of the solitary walk and the horrible ghouls; but her will was as strong as her trust in God.

Elise went, but the king and the archbishop followed her. They saw her disappear within the grated gateway of the churchyard. When they followed they saw the ghouls sitting on the gravestone as Elise had seen them before; and the king turned away his head because he thought she was among them, she whose head this very evening had rested on his breast.

"The people must judge her," he groaned, and the people judged. "Let her be consumed in the glowing flames!"

She was led away from her beautiful royal apartments to a dark, damp dungeon, where the wind whistled through the grated window. Instead of velvet and silk they gave her the bundle of nettles she had gathered to lay her head upon. The hard burning shirts of mail were to be her covering, but they could have given her nothing more precious.

She set to work again with many prayers to God. Outside her prison the street boys sang derisive songs about her, and not a soul comforted her with a kind word.

Towards evening she heard the rustle of swans' wings close to her window. It was her youngest brother; at last he had found her. He sobbed aloud with joy, although he knew that the coming night might be her last, but then her work was almost done and her brothers were there.

The archbishop came to spend her last hours with her, as he had promised the king. She shook her head at him, and

33

by looks and gestures begged him to leave her. She had
only this night in which to finish her work, or else all would
be wasted, all—her pain, tears, and sleepless nights. The
archbishop went away with bitter words against her, but
poor Elise knew that she was innocent, and she went on

with her work.

The little mice ran about the floor bringing nettles to her feet, so as to give what help they could, and a thrush sat on the grating of the window where he sang all night, as merrily as he could, to keep up her courage.

It was still only dawn, and the sun would not rise for an hour, when the eleven brothers stood at the gate of the palace, begging to be taken to the king. This could not be done, was the answer, for it was still night; the king was asleep and no one dared wake him. All their entreaties and threats were useless. The watch turned out and even the king himself came to see what was the matter; but just then the sun rose, and no more brothers were to be seen—only the eleven wild swans hovering over the palace.

The whole populace streamed out of the town gates— they were all anxious to see the witch burnt. A miserable horse drew the cart in which Elise was seated. They had put upon her a smock of green sacking, and all her beautiful long hair hung loose from the lovely head. Her cheeks were deathly pale, and her lips moved softly, while her fingers unceasingly twisted the green yarn. Even on the way to her death she could not abandon her unfinished work. Ten shirts lay completed at her feet—she laboured away at the eleventh, amid the scoffing insults of the populace.

"Look at the witch, how she mutters. She has never a book of psalms in her hands, no, there she sits with her loathsome sorcery. Tear it away from her into a thousand bits!"

The crowd pressed around her to destroy her work, but just then eleven white swans flew down and perched upon the cart flapping their wings. The crowd gave way before them in terror.

"It is a sign from heaven! She is innocent!" they whispered, but they dared not say it aloud.

The executioner seized her by the hand, but she hastily threw the eleven shirts over the swans, who were immediately transformed to eleven handsome princes; but the youngest had a swan's wing in place of an arm, for one sleeve was wanting to his shirt of mail; she had not been able to finish it.

"Now I may speak! I am innocent."

The populace who saw what had happened bowed down before her as if she had been a saint, but she sank lifeless in her brothers' arms; so great had been the strain, the terror, and the suffering she had endured.

"Yes, innocent she is indeed," said the eldest brother, and he told them all that had happened.

Whilst he spoke a wonderful fragrance spread around, as of millions of roses. Every faggot in the pile had taken root and shot out branches, and a great high hedge of red roses had arisen. At the very top was one pure white blossom; it shone like a star, and the king broke it off and laid it on Elise's bosom, and she woke with joy and peace in her heart.

All the church bells began to ring of their own accord, and the singing birds flocked around them. Surely such a bridal procession went back to the palace as no king had ever seen before!

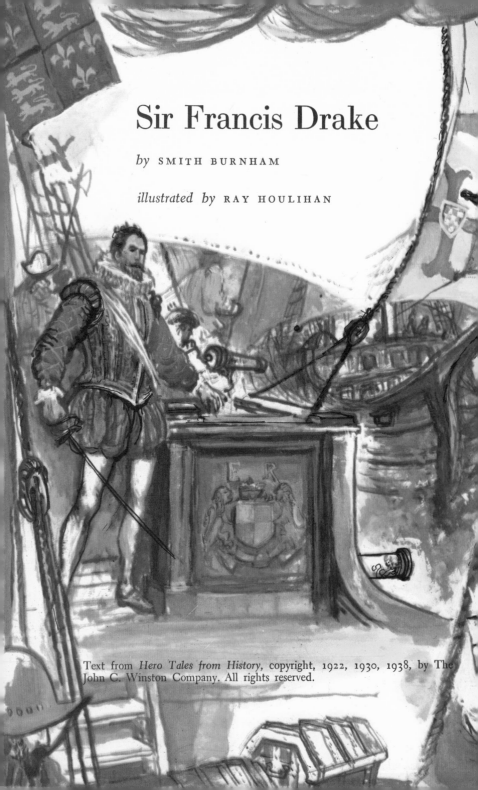

Sir Francis Drake

by SMITH BURNHAM

illustrated by RAY HOULIHAN

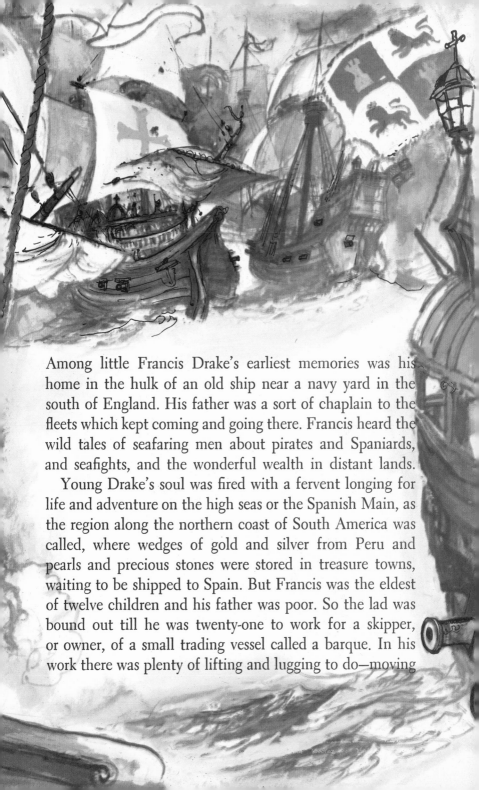

Among little Francis Drake's earliest memories was his home in the hulk of an old ship near a navy yard in the south of England. His father was a sort of chaplain to the fleets which kept coming and going there. Francis heard the wild tales of seafaring men about pirates and Spaniards, and seafights, and the wonderful wealth in distant lands.

Young Drake's soul was fired with a fervent longing for life and adventure on the high seas or the Spanish Main, as the region along the northern coast of South America was called, where wedges of gold and silver from Peru and pearls and precious stones were stored in treasure towns, waiting to be shipped to Spain. But Francis was the eldest of twelve children and his father was poor. So the lad was bound out till he was twenty-one to work for a skipper, or owner, of a small trading vessel called a barque. In his work there was plenty of lifting and lugging to do—moving

baskets and bales on and off his master's boat. He had to work long hours—often at night. His food was scarce and coarse and his pay was very small indeed, for his work was thought not worth much more than his learning the sailor trade.

Sometimes they sailed the barque across the Channel to France or Holland and brought back a cargo to England; but that was as far as such a small craft could be trusted to go. Francis often saw great ships riding high on their majestic way to foreign lands, and he felt sure that those lucky sailors would have thrilling times with pirates and Spaniards, and come home loaded down with gold and silver, spices, precious gems, and thrilling stories. Much as he yearned to go on a long voyage, the faithful fellow stayed by his master, worked hard, and learned all the ins and outs of sailing a ship, whether large or small.

Just before Francis was old enough to be his own man the good skipper died. As he had never married and had

no near relatives, he left his barque to his faithful apprentice. Young Drake continued the business, running from port to port and market to market for about a year, when he saw a chance to sail on a longer voyage and engage in a larger enterprise. He had a cousin, John Hawkins, who was captain of a vessel. This cousin now had a little fleet of five ships and was about to engage in the slave trade. As Francis had learned to manage a ship, Captain Hawkins offered to put the smallest vessel in his fleet under his young cousin's command. So Francis sold his barque and became captain of his cousin's ship *Judith*.

Now, at the age of twenty-two, Francis Drake was embarking on the voyage of life with the prospect of great

adventures, as he had always dreamed of doing. Slave trading was not considered wrong four hundred years ago. The ships would go to Africa and buy or carry off Negroes and take them to some foreign country to work in fields and mines. There the slaves would be sold for gold, silver, pearls, and other things of great value. Sometimes the owner of a fleet would make a fortune in a single adventure. Of course, there was a great risk to run. Although England and Spain were not then at war, the English and Spanish treated each other as enemies when they met on the high seas.

For this voyage, Captain Hawkins got leave of Queen Elizabeth "to load Negroes in Guinea and sell them in the West Indies." As a sign that the hundred and seventy men on Hawkins's fleet saw nothing wrong in stealing black men from their homes and selling them to be slaves, here is a motto which that captain had written to govern his soldiers and sailors: "Serve God daily, love one another, preserve your victuals, beware of fire, and keep good company."

Hawkins and Drake seem to have had no trouble in seizing Negroes on the coast of Africa, or in selling their human cargo in the Spanish ports of America. But as these slavers were starting back to England they were caught in a storm and had to go into a harbor in Mexico for safety

and to repair damages. While they were there a Spanish fleet five times as large as theirs, loaded with gold and pearls, came in also for repairs. The English agreed to leave the Spaniards without touching their ships if the Spaniards would let them alone. But the Spanish captain did not keep his word and there was a fierce battle. Hawkins and Drake did great damage to the Spanish fleet. They reached England safely with two of their ships, though they had lost nearly all the treasure they had received as pay for the slaves.

Captain Drake complained to the queen of the way in which the Spaniards had deceived them, but she was afraid to go to war with a country which had such a powerful navy as Spain's was then. So the bold English captain took matters into his own hands. He made one voyage after another, attacking Spanish settlements where gold and silver were stored, boarding Spanish vessels, killing the men or taking them prisoners, and bringing their rich cargoes to England. Within a few years the Spaniards lived in terror of their lives when they heard that Francis Drake

was near, and the king of Spain appealed to Queen Elizabeth to stop those attacks, calling Drake "the master thief of the western world."

On one of these expeditions, Drake landed on the Isthmus of Panama, or Darien as it was then called. Some of the natives showed him the way across to the South Sea, or the Pacific Ocean as Magellan had named it; and when they had ascended a mountain about half-way across, Drake climbed a tall tree from which he gazed upon the broad, unexplored ocean.

"May God give me leave and life to sail that sea but once!" murmured Captain Drake to his companions.

But Queen Elizabeth had heard of the terror of the Spaniards and ordered him to stop, lest he plunge her kingdom into a Spanish war before England was ready. So for a while Francis Drake stayed at home and suffered because he was not allowed to fight with the Spaniards.

About five years after his first sight of the Pacific, Captain Drake sailed away from England in command of a fleet of five vessels of which the flagship was the *Golden Hind*. The object of the voyage was a secret. This was about sixty years after Magellan, the Portuguese master-sailor, had discovered and passed through the straits named for him.

It took five months for the fleet to reach the eastern

coast of South America. In due time they found and passed through the Straits of Magellan; but the ocean beyond was more terrific than Pacific, for a fierce storm drove the *Golden Hind* even farther south than Tierra del Fuego, so that Drake was first to land at Cape Horn, the southernmost point of South America. At the place where the waters of the Atlantic meet those of the Pacific, Drake lay down and embraced the sharp point of rock and exclaimed: "I am the only man in the world who has ever been so far south!"

All the ships in Drake's fleet but the *Golden Hind* had either been sunk, broken, or scattered. Now at last he had "leave and life to sail that sea but once"—with one ship alone. The undaunted hero sailed up the western coast of South America to capture treasure from the gold mines of Peru. When he came near Valparaiso, some Spaniards in a ship saw the *Golden Hind* approach. Never dreaming that an English ship could be in that ocean, they were astonished to see a gun presented through a porthole and to hear an English voice calling on them roughly to surrender. So they stared and cursed under their breath while "the master thief of the western world" took charge of their ship with sixty thousand gold pesos, jewels, merchandise, and a stock of wine.

When the people of Valparaiso heard that the dreadful Drake was in their harbor, they fled from the city. The little English crew entered the town, and stocked up with bread, bacon, and wine, which they enjoyed to the full after many months of famishing. In a day or two the *Golden Hind* sailed away northward toward Peru.

At another port they waylaid three unguarded barques and captured fifty-seven bricks of silver, each weighing about twenty pounds. When they came to the port of Lima, there were seventeen vessels anchored in the harbor. Not daunted by numbers, Drake sailed right into the harbor, captured them all with his one ship, and made their men prisoners while he plundered the whole Spanish fleet. By this time the alarm had been spread along the coast that Drake was capturing everything in sight, and the governor of Peru with two thousand men was waiting for him at Callao.

Drake's good luck seemed now to desert him. In the pres-

ence of that waiting army the wind died down and the *Golden Hind* was becalmed, helpless, and unable to move a yard. The Spanish governor grinned as he went out in boats from the shore with four hundred soldiers, to take back all the precious cargo Drake had lately captured. But before the armed men reached the English ship a gale blew up and Drake sailed away, laughing and waving farewells to his pursuers.

The cargo from the last ship they captured overloaded the *Golden Hind* with tons of gold, silver, and precious gems. It was useless to overhaul any more galleons, for they now had all their ship could carry. Their only thought was to get their treasure home safe and sound. Sailing across the Pacific, they were sixty-eight days without sighting land.

The *Golden Hind* began to show the strain of her long voyage; so they set up a forge on an island in the South Pacific and spent weeks in making repairs, so that the ship might complete her voyage around the world. After they had sailed more than a month longer, the ship ran on a ledge of rocks. Seeing that they could not get her off, they threw six cannon overboard, then the sugar and spices, then great fortunes in silver. At last they managed to work her off the ledge into deep water. Still it was nearly a year before they reached the harbor of Plymouth, England.

The wildest dreams of the boy Francis Drake were now more than realized. All England buzzed with his astounding exploits. The city bells rang and there was a general holiday, with feasting and dancing. Queen Elizabeth came down from London and dined with the great captain on the *Golden Hind*. Before she left the deck, the captain knelt before her and she tapped him on the shoulder with his sword, thus knighting him Sir Francis Drake.

After this the greatest of the English knights of the high seas made many voyages, dealing out destruction to Spanish galleons and treasure stores. He attacked cities and burned fleets—reporting to the queen that he had just "singed the

Spanish king's beard." Drake was one of the four chiefs in command of the English ships that destroyed the Spanish Armada. No one did more than he to take the sea power away from Spain and give it to England, and thus make it possible for the English to begin the settlement of our country.

Timothy Titus

by BLANCHE ELLIOTT

illustrated by NINON

Timothy Titus Butteryjill
Had a red-roofed house at the foot of a hill,
And the hill rose up all green and brown
Like an ice-cream cone turned upside down.
And Timothy's house had a rosebush rack
And a porch at the front.
And a porch at the back.

And Timothy had no sister or brother,
But he had a house and he had a mother.
And once when the summer sun arose
Timothy woke and put on his clothes.
He tiptoed softly down the stair
But he couldn't find Mother anywhere.
He looked in the kitchen,
The cellar,
And hall,
He couldn't find Mother at all, at all.

He hurried quickly back up the stair.
Timothy's mother
Was not there.
Then away outdoors where the back door led
Tim looked in the garden, and rabbit shed,
And in the garage,
But it was bare.
And back to the kitchen. She wasn't there.
Then Timothy ran where the colts were kicking.
"For maybe," he said, "she's berry picking."

He saw an arm. He surely had her.
It was just a man with an apple ladder.
Then he heard a step that he felt somehow
Would surely be Mother.
It was a cow.

He was rounding a bush when he felt a peck
Like his mother's kiss on the back of his neck,
On the back of his neck away up high,
He turned.
It was only a butterfly.

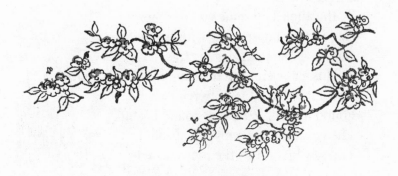

Then something moved in a billowy heap.
He hurried closer.
It was some sheep.
And Timothy searched both there and here,
But Timothy's mother was nowhere near.

By this time Tim some way or other
Had lost his house along with his mother.
And on Tim ran in ziggety zags
Till his legs were scratched and his clothes were rags.
And Timothy Titus Butteryjill
Found himself 'way, 'way round his hill.
Then quickly, suddenly, up ahead
Tim saw his house—the roof was red—

And his front porch with the rosebush rack.
(Don't you remember he left from the back?)
And Timothy ran, just lickety splitting.
His mother was on the front porch knitting.

60

Georgie

written and illustrated

by ROBERT BRIGHT

In a little village in New England there was a little house
which belonged to Mr. and Mrs. Whittaker.
Up in the little attic of this little house there lived a little
ghost. His name was Georgie.

61

Every night at the
same time he gave the
loose board on the stairs
a little creak
And the parlor door a
little squeak

And then Mr. and Mrs. Whittaker knew it was
time to go to bed.
And Herman, the cat, he knew it was time to prowl.

And as for Miss Oliver, the owl, she knew it was time to
wake up and say "Whoo-oo-oo!"
And so it went with everything as it should be,
until Mr. Whittaker took it into his head to hammer
a nail into the loose board on the stairs
And to oil the hinges of the parlor door.

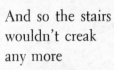

And so the stairs
wouldn't creak
any more

And the door
wouldn't squeak
any more

And Mr. and Mrs. Whittaker didn't know when it was time to go to bed any more

And Herman, he didn't know when it was time to begin to prowl any more.

And as for Miss Oliver, she didn't know when
to wake up any more and went on sleeping.

And Georgie sat up
in the attic and
moped.
That was a fine
how-do-you-do!

Pretty soon, though, Georgie decided to find some other
house to haunt. But while he ran to this house
And then to that house

Each house already had a ghost.

The only house in the
whole village which didn't
have a ghost was Mr.
Gloams' place. But that
was so awfully gloomy!

The big door *groaned* so!

And the
big stairway
moaned so!

And besides Mr. Gloams himself was such a crotchety
old man, he came near frightening Georgie half to death.
So Georgie ran away to a cow barn where there lived a
harmless cow.

But the cow paid no attention to Georgie. She just
chewed her cud all the time, and it wasn't much fun.
Meanwhile a lot of time went by and it rained a good
deal. And during the winter it snowed to beat the band

And out at the cow barn Georgie was terribly cold and uncomfortable.

BUT what with the dampness from
the rain and the coldness from the snow,
something happened to that board on
the Whittaker stairs and to the hinges on
the Whittaker parlor door.

It was Herman who discovered it and told Miss Oliver.
And she woke up with a start.
Miss Oliver flew right over to the cow barn to tell Georgie
that the board on the stairs was loose again, and that the
hinges on the parlor door were rusty again.

What glad
tidings that was
for Georgie!
He ran right
home lickety-split.

WELCOME

And so, at the same
old time, the stairs
creaked again

And the parlor
door squeaked
again

And Mr. and Mrs. Whittaker knew when it was
time to go to sleep again

And Herman, he knew when
to begin to prowl again.

And as for Miss Oliver, she knew when it was time to wake up again and say "Whoo-oo-oo!"
Thank goodness!

A Horse
for a Prince

retold by JAMES BALDWIN

illustrated by DON FREEMAN

There was in the northern part of Greece a land called Macedon. In ancient times this land was ruled over by a warlike king named Philip.

One day King Philip bought a fine horse called Bucephalus. He was a noble animal, and the king paid a very high price for him. But he was wild and savage, and no man could mount him, or do anything at all with him.

Text of "Alexander and Bucephalus", from *Fifty Famous Stories Retold*.

They tried to whip him, but that only made him worse. At last the king bade his servants take him away.

"It is a pity to ruin so fine a horse as that," said Alexander, the king's young son. "Those men do not know how to treat him."

"Perhaps you can do better than they," said his father scornfully.

"I know," said Alexander, "that if you would only give me leave to try I could manage this horse better than anyone else."

"And if you fail to do so, what then?" asked Philip.

"I will pay you the price of the horse," said the lad.

While everybody was laughing, Alexander ran up to Bucephalus, and turned his head toward the sun. He had noticed that the horse was afraid of his own shadow.

He then spoke gently to the horse, and patted him with
his hand. When he had quieted him a little, he made a
quick spring, and leaped upon the horse's back.

Everybody expected to see the boy killed outright. But
he kept his seat, and let the horse run as fast as he would.
By and by, when Bucephalus had become tired, Alexander
reined him in, and rode back to the place where his father
was standing.

All the men who were there shouted when they saw that the boy had proved himself to be the master of the horse.

He leaped to the ground, and his father ran and kissed him.

"My son," said the king, "Macedon is too small a place for you. You must seek a larger kingdom that will be worthy of you."

After that, Alexander and Bucephalus were the best of friends. They were said to be always together, for when one of them was seen, the other was sure to be not far away. But the horse would never allow any one to mount him but his master.

Alexander became the most famous king and warrior that was ever known; and for that reason he is always called Alexander the Great. Bucephalus carried him through many countries and in many fierce battles, and more than once did he save his master's life.

ROBIN

EASTERN BLUEBIRD

SCARLET
TANAGER

GOLDEN-CROWNED KINGLET

Feeding the Birds This Winter

by ROBERT S. LEMMON

illustrated by ALEXANDROFF

FOODS THAT BIRDS LIKE

When winter comes the small wild birds need plenty of
food to keep them warm. You know how much better *you*
feel after breakfast or lunch on a freezing day! It is the
same way with birds. Good food in their stomachs gives
them strength as well as warmth. It is a little like shoveling
coal into a furnace or putting oil in an oil burner.

Probably you will see a few wild birds like Sparrows,
Juncos and Chickadees around your yard in early October
or even sooner than that. They may be in the bushes, trees
or right on the ground. If they find food that they like they
will come back day after day. In a week or so other birds
from around the neighborhood will come, too. The first
thing you know there may be quite a flock, especially in

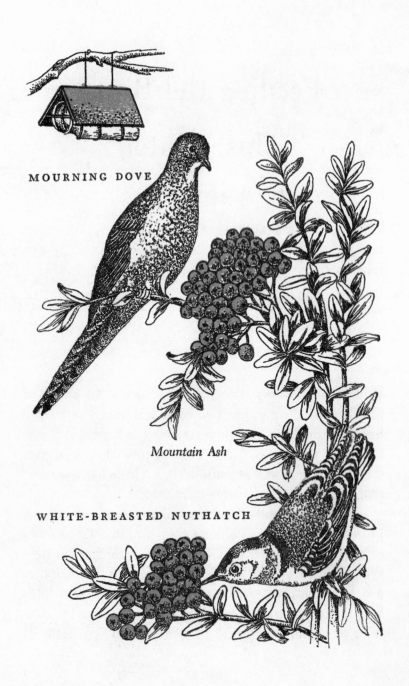

MOURNING DOVE

Mountain Ash

WHITE-BREASTED NUTHATCH

the early morning and late in the afternoon. Some people who live in the country and feed birds regularly have more than a hundred visitors every day by the time New Year's Day comes along. It is not at all unusual for them to see twenty different kinds before spring comes again.

Different sorts of birds like different foods. All of the sparrow and junco family feast on small seeds and crushed grains. So do Mourning Doves and Towhees. Sunflower seeds are perfect for the handsome Blue Jays, Cardinals, Chickadees, Nuthatches, and several others. Chunks of beef suet are sure to attract Chickadees, Nuthatches, Carolina Wrens, and all of the Woodpeckers. Peanut butter is a favorite of most of these suet-eaters, but it is quite expensive if you have many birds to feed.

Nearly all of the "special mixtures" sold for wild birds are too high-priced because they contain a good many seeds which will never be eaten. So there is a lot of waste. Experienced bird feeders save money and get dozens of bird visitors by giving them "baby chick scratch feed." This is a ground-up mixture of corn, wheat, barley and oat seeds. It is made especially for very young chickens, but many of our wild birds love it and will eat up every last smitch. The best place to get this fine food is a store which sells regular poultry and other farm animal supplies.

Many leftovers from your own kitchen can be used, too. Stale pieces of bread, cake and crackers, broken into small pieces, are just the ticket for many wild birds. All of them are still better if flavored with some of the hot grease left over in the frying pan.

Old peanuts, either in or out of their shells, are welcome

tidbits for Blue Jays and Nuthatches. These birds are also fond of small meat scraps. A steak, lamb or roast beef bone, with bits of meat sticking to it, will help a Jay, Nuthatch or Woodpecker for days if you tie it to the trunk or large branch of a tree. Pieces of orange, apple, banana or some other fruit which has started to go bad are very likely to be eagerly eaten by birds unless the weather is so cold that it freezes them hard. Sometimes dried currants and raisins are welcomed, too.

Some of these foods might not be easy for us to digest. But the wild birds which come to your yard will have no trouble with them if their crops, or "stomachs", contain some coarse sand. You see, this sand grinds up the larger pieces of food. While the ground is bare the birds can find all the grinding stuff they need. It is another story, though, when deep snow is everywhere for days or maybe weeks. At such times the feathered fellows will be delighted if you give them some "bird gravel" to help their digestions. A small box of this can be bought at any cage-bird store.

Most birds drink a good deal of water for their size. While the weather is mild they can usually find as much as they want. But when everything is frozen hard outdoors they may get very thirsty. So, when real cold comes, it is a good idea to give them a dish of hot water at the same time that you put out fresh food. It is worth doing this several times a day if you can.

The simplest way to feed the seed-eating winter birds is to scatter their meal on the ground. This works quite well when there is no snow. Be sure to choose a place which is several yards from the nearest bushes through which a cat

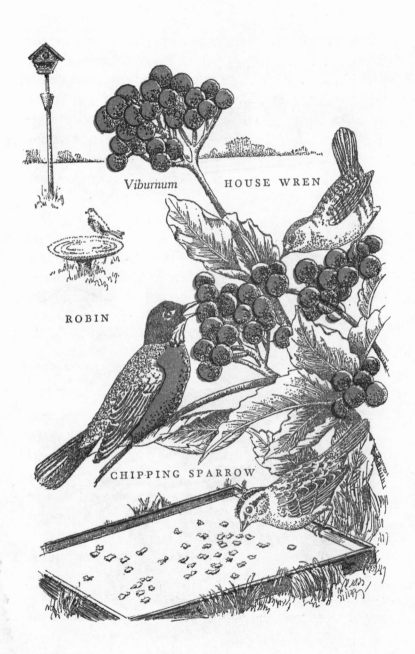

Viburnum HOUSE WREN

ROBIN

CHIPPING SPARROW

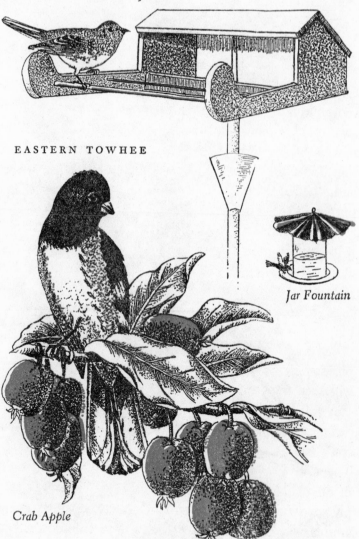

SLATE-COLORED JUNCO

Weather-vane Feeder

EASTERN TOWHEE

Jar Fountain

Crab Apple

might sneak and pounce on them before they have a chance
to fly away.

BIRD FEEDING STATIONS

Of course, this ground-feeding idea will not work well in
snowy weather. Then the snow must be either brushed
away or the food put where it will not be buried. This
means that you will have to find some other place to set
the dinner table. There are many kinds of boxes, shelves
and other containers which can be made or bought for this
purpose. Let's look at some of them.

The simplest kind is a flat wooden tray with a rim around
it to keep the food from falling off. This should have a roof
at least twice as wide to catch most of the snow and rain.
It can be set on top of a post about five feet high. Sometimes it is easier to hang it by a thin wire from the branch
of a tree. There should be several large holes in the bottom
of the tray to prevent flooding by rain or melting snow. A
piece of copper window-screen wire tacked under each hole
will keep the food from falling through.

A still better feeder has a watertight glass box or upside-
down jar between the tray and the roof. This is filled with
seeds which can come out at the bottom and onto the tray.
The seeds keep slipping down as the birds eat. One filling
of the container often lasts for several days. The food supply stays dry even in a bad storm. Some of these feeders
are made so that they can be hung from brackets fastened
to the house or the trunk of a tree. Others are mounted on

posts. And still others are hung from the branches of trees.

Seed feeders made to be placed just outside of a window are the most fun because they give you such wonderful close-up views of the hungry birds which come to them. There are many kinds of these eating places. All of them are open at the front so that the birds can come and go easily. They usually have glass on the side next to the window, to give you a good view from indoors. Some of the best ones have glass ends and tops, too.

There is only one trouble with these window-sill bird feeders. Every now and then you have to clean all the glass in them. You see, it often gets spattered by rain and the scratching and fluttering of the birds inside the box. But cleaning it is not much of a chore.

One of the best of all feeders is the weather-vane kind. This is a wooden box with a long "tail" which sticks out behind like a weather vane. It is balanced on top of a strong pole so that it can turn in any direction and always face the wind. This keeps the snow from blowing into it and burying the food. The birds come and go easily through the wide-open back of the box where the "tail" begins. The best kinds have glass windows in the sides and sometimes the front. This is because birds generally do not like to go into any box where they cannot see out in all directions.

Well-made weather-vane feeders are quite expensive to buy, but they will last for years if you keep them well painted. The best posts for supporting them are made of metal.

Woodpeckers and other birds which like beef suet and other fatty things should have different kinds of feeders.

COMMON
GOLDFINCH

Window-shelf Feeder

Fire-thorn

SLATE-COLORED JUNCO

COMMON
SAPSUCKER

WILSON'S WARBLER

One of the best is a square stick about two inches thick and a foot or so long. Shallow holes are bored into all four sides of it from top to bottom. Each of these holds a little paper cup filled with a suet and small seed mixture. When the cups have been emptied you put in fresh ones.

One end of this feeder has a metal ring so that you can hang it from a tree branch or bracket. The whole "feeding stick", and plenty of loaded cups for refilling it, can be bought in most stores which sell wild bird supplies. Very often you can find what you want in a regular hardware store.

Pieces of ordinary suet can be tied to tree trunks or strong branches where the Woodpeckers and other birds can peck away at them easily. The trouble with this plan is that when some of the suet has been eaten the rest may fall out from under the string. It is much better to put the fat in a strong wire cage through which the birds' bills can reach it easily. Holders of this sort are sold in bird supply stores. They can be hung on wires or nailed against tree trunks.

Very often a suet holder is fastened to a seed feeder in one way or another. This idea is a good one which the birds will really like. It means, too, that more kinds of birds will learn to come to the same dining room. Such double-duty feeders can be bought ready-made. Or you can just tie a suet chunk to a regular seed feeder in some way. You may be sure that the Woodpeckers and Chickadees will find it.

If there are wild Gray Squirrels around your home they will probably steal as much of the birds' food as they can.

They are very clever about this, and will surprise you by their skill in climbing and jumping to feeders which you think are far out of their reach.

If your feeder is on an ordinary pole five feet or more above the ground a Gray Squirrel can easily climb up to it. This can usually be stopped by cutting a hole in the bottom of a metal wastebasket and fastening it upside down on the pole a few inches below the feeder. The squirrel will climb as far as the basket but cannot go any farther. He will try and try to get through or around it, but finally has to give up the idea. Squirrel "baffles" of various kinds will do just as good a job, if you don't want to bother to make your own out of a wastebasket.

All feeders, by the way, should be at least fifteen feet away from the nearest tree trunk or large branch. Otherwise some daring Gray Squirrel may reach them by a tremendous jump. Remember this even if your feeder is the hanging kind. Thin copper wire is the best thing on which to hang it from a branch. If you used string the squirrels could easily climb up and down it. An extra-smart one might even chew through the string and let the whole thing tumble to the ground where he could eat every bit of the food.

Here is another good winter feeding idea:

When you are through with the family Christmas tree, don't just throw it away! You see, it can easily be made into a first-class holiday gift for the wild birds. First, stand it up outdoors where it will not be blown down. Then fasten a lot of bird food to its branches. Stale doughnuts tied on with pieces of string are splendid. So are peanuts, shells and all. These should be hung on pieces of thin thread which the

Suet Feeder

DOWNY
WOODPECKER

BLUE JAY

English Yew

Tree Box-feeder

CARDINAL

CATBIRD

Euonymus

Blue Jays can break easily. Then these big, beautiful birds will carry the nuts away in their bills to a tree where they can peck them open and eat the tidbits inside.

Raisins tied to the branches in the same way are very good, too. Several kinds of winter birds are crazy about them. Dried pine cones well smeared with partly melted suet are also great favorites. When they have been strongly tied to the tree so that they can swing in the wind the chickadees will feast on them until every bit of suet is gone.

NATURE'S FEEDING STATIONS

Besides the seeds and other foods that you put out for the winter birds, there are many which can be grown outdoors if you have a good-sized yard. They grow naturally on certain trees, bushes and vines. When these plants get started the birds will quickly find the feasts which are ready and waiting for them every fall and even into the winter. Some of the best kinds of trees that provide birds with fruit, berries, and seeds are Yellow and Cherry Birches, Flowering Dogwood, Hawthorn, Flowering Crab Apple, and Mountain Ash

Some pretty bushes, too, provide the birds with fine fruit meals in the fall or winter. Among the best ones are bush honeysuckles of different kinds, the Winged Euonymus, Viburnums, and Winterberry.

All of these bushes I have told you about will live through very cold winters. So they are good ones to plant even in cold northern states.

There are also some vines whose fruit is eagerly eaten by winter birds. One of the best is Hall's Honeysuckle. Another good bird vine is the high-climbing Virginia Creeper. This has small bluish berries which help to keep many a winter bird warm and strong. There is just one trouble with these two handsome vines. They grow so fast and far that they may take over your whole place if you don't watch out.

All through the year our wild birds like to have safe places to sleep and to escape from the enemies like some hawks and tame cats. During the summer, when green leaves are everywhere, almost any tree, bush or vine gives them good protection at night as well as during the day. But when these leaves drop in the fall the birds are not so lucky. Just the same, you can do something about it. By planting a few evergreens around the place you can make life much safer and more comfortable for them. This means that you will have more birds to eat the meals which you fix for them.

Evergreen trees, like pines, hemlocks, spruces and Red Cedar, are first-rate hiding and sleeping places by day as well as at night. They help the birds keep warm, too, by sheltering them from the wind.

Several of the evergreen bushes are just as good, or even better. One of the best of these is the Japanese Yew. Also, this rugged bush or small tree bears red fruits which many birds gladly eat.

The very spiny, thick-growing Fire-thorn, or Pyracantha, gives splendid protection. Some varieties of it may grow fifteen feet tall. Others are only half that high. All of them have many stiff, thorny branches. No cat or hawk could ever get into one of these bushes, but small birds, like Juncos and Sparrows, have no trouble. These little fellows sleep there in perfect safety all winter.

Another good thing about the Fire-thorn is that south of Pennsylvania and New York it keeps its green leaves all winter. This shuts out cold winds and even snow. The bushes have great bunches of bright red berries, too, which are beautiful all through the fall and far into the winter.

FEEDING BIRDS IS FUN

Even without any evergreen trees or shrubs you can easily make a first-class year-round shelter for birds. All you need to do is to pile a lot of dead branches in some place where the heap cannot be seen from the house. The bigger the pile, the better it will be liked by Sparrows and other ground-feeding winter birds. They will sleep there at night, and often feed on the ground under it during the day.

Any fair-sized branches cut from trees or shrubs will be all right for making one of these "brush-pile" bird shelters. New branches should be added to the top every year. These will make up for those older ones at the bottom which have rotted away.

The most important time to start feeding wild birds is when the leaves start falling in early autumn. This will give the little fellows a chance to get used to the idea before winter weather starts. In a little while some of them will like the plan so much that they will stay around all winter.

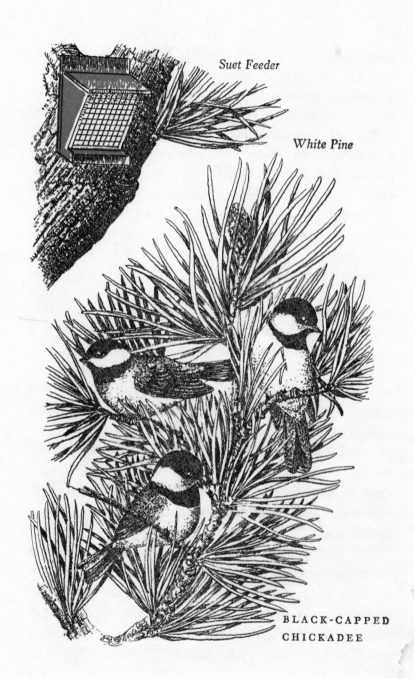

Suet Feeder

White Pine

BLACK-CAPPED
CHICKADEE

Many people keep up the feeding all through the year. This can be special fun because most of the birds which come in for meals in the spring and summer will be different from the cold-weather ones.

You will learn many interesting things about wild birds as you watch those which come to eat the food you have put out for them. For instance, most kinds eat several good meals every day. The favorite hours for this are about sunrise, in the middle of the morning, noontime, the middle of the afternoon, and toward sunset. Some kinds, though, have their first breakfast so early that there is hardly enough daylight for you to see them. These early risers, also, have a final snack a half-hour or more after sunset. By that time many of the other kinds are sound asleep!

Another queer fact is that certain sorts of birds are always quarreling among themselves while others never do. There are bullies as well as fraidy-cats even in these small feathered creatures. Some kinds are greedy, too, and really stuff themselves with as much food as they can swallow. Others eat much less at a time, but come in more often for a meal.

You will also learn a great deal about how and where different birds find their food. Some eat on the ground, others above it. Some walk, some hop, some run, some climb. Each kind has its own habits and sticks pretty closely to them. And that is true all through the whole tremendous kingdom of the birds.

The War Whoop
of the Wily Iroquois

by MARTHA KELLER

illustrated by ROBERT MACLEAN

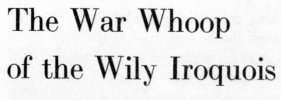

FOR MARTHA AND RANDA—
WITH REGRET THAT THEY ARE OLDER NOW.

*This is their father's story—not mine. I have only retold it.
It is based on a true account of a real Indian raid that he
found in an old copy of* The Connecticut Gazette *and*
The Universal Intelligencer, *dated September 29, 1780.*

(When this story is read aloud those who are listening
should warwhoop whenever the Indians do. But remember,
it must be wild and shrill and menacing. If it is not, it is
just noise.)

Pioneering is the path that one man makes to a cabin and a clearing in a forest of dark trees.

It is these: burned stumps, ploughed land, pulled weeds —long gun, thin knife, broad axe—picking up the boulder stones, working in the garden patch—and the WAR WHOOP of the wily Iroquois.

In pioneering, small things—like forgetting to carry water in a bucket from the brook—can be very dangerous.

If you are doing any fighting—if you are in an Indian raid, for instance—you can last for a long time without food. But not without water.

That was the one thing that once all the Dexters forgot.

They forgot because they were thinking about other things.

John Dexter was thinking that someday soon he'd have to make some lead bullets and buy some powder for his long rifle.

Anne Dexter was thinking how pretty her blue teapot looked on the big mantel.

Jim was admiring in his mind the new knife his father had just made him from the blade of an old saw.

And little Sue was too busy singing to think much of anything because she was too fond of singing to think much when she sang.

The reason they were all thinking of something else was that they didn't much like what they were doing.

John was hoeing weeds in the garden patch. Anne and Jim and Sue were all picking bugs.

And then, far down the little valley to the South, John heard a little hoot owl go *towheeeeeeheeeee*. And then over the hill to the East he heard another little hoot owl go *towheeeeeheeeee*. But he didn't stop any longer to listen. He said, "Anne, go in the cabin and take Sue with you." And then he said to Jim, who was near him, "Tell your mother to lift down the gun."

And he went right on hoeing as if he hadn't heard anything so no one looking at him would think he was worried or in a hurry. But he hoed right up to the cabin and leaned his hoe up against the logs. And went in.

Because that *towheeeeeheeeee* meant Indians.

So he knew that pretty soon he would hear something else—the WAR WHOOP of the wily Iroquois.

As he came in the door, Anne handed him the long rifle that hung over the fireplace, and she said, "There's no water. There were only *two* hoot-owl hoots so they're not all around us yet. You cover me with the gun, and I'll fill the bucket."

So she stepped out the door with the bucket in her hand and went down to the brook. And John stood just inside the door, in the shadow, watching and watching and watching for Indians. And ready to shoot.

Anne didn't hurry because she didn't want any Indians lurking near to know she knew they were lurking. But she didn't waste time either. And she didn't look to right or left, for fear she would see them. She just went right ahead —humming a little.

But when she reached the brook—where the water there made so much noise that she couldn't hear anything but its rushing and its roaring—she filled the bucket very fast, and started back.

Just as she got near the cabin door she saw the axe stuck in the chopping block, and she leaned over to pick it up and carry it back in with her, thinking—we might need that. And as she leaned over to pick up the axe an arrow whistled over her head. And she heard it sing and ping as it struck the big plank door, and saw it swing and sway there—and shiver and swish and shake where it stuck.

John fired his gun. And the Indian on the path behind her fell dead.

And all around the cabin, in the green vines, and the thick brush, and the dead stumps, and the dark trees they heard—the WAR WHOOP of the wily Iroquois.

They shut the door and bolted it.

And Anne put down her bucket and panted a little and said, "Jim, you and Sue get down behind the bed between the bed and the wall, and stay there, and keep still."

Then, while Indian arrows and Indian bullets ripped and thudded against the thick log walls, John fired and fired and fired again—through the front window. Anne kept watch through the other little window. And handed him bullets, and powder, and patches for his gun.

And all the while, from every side of the cabin, from the green vines, and the thick brush, and the dead stumps, and the dark trees they heard—the WAR WHOOP of the wily Iroquois.

John fired his gun so much that after a bit he began to run out of ammunition—and he got very worried

But about that time the Indians set fire to the little shed where he kept his seed, and his hay, and his plough, and his wheelbarrow. The hay made the fire blaze high with sparks, and thick smoke from the burning shed swept and swirled around the cabin like fog

When John saw the smoke swirling and the sparks flying, he knew the Indians were busy. So while the wily Iroquois whooped and hollered by the burning shed, he opened the door of the cabin just a crack—and peeped out

And almost at the door of the cabin he saw the bodies of three dead Indians. One of them had only a bow and arrows. But the other two had guns.

So while the smoke hid the cabin, Anne covered *him* with the rifle.

And he slipped out the door and cut the powder horns that held their powder, and the little deerskin bags that held their lead, from the bodies of the two dead Indians. And ran back in with the powder horns and bullet bags in his hands.

And then, together, he and Anne slammed the door shut and bolted it again.

And still they heard—through the sparks flying, and smoke swirling, and the gun roaring, and the door shaking —the WAR WHOOP of the wily Iroquois.

Jim and Sue lay very still and very quiet between the bed and the wall. But while they were lying there so very quiet and so very still, Jim took his new knife and he poked a little hole in the thick mud that was plastered between the logs of the cabin to make them fit tight. It wasn't a big hole, but he and Sue could *see*. And when they looked out they saw an Indian had crept so close to the cabin they could almost touch him.

So they yelled, "MA! HEY, MA!"

That was why, when the Indian stuck his gun through the one little window so he could fire at John who was shooting out of the other—Anne was ready. She took the axe and smashed the barrel of the Indian's gun so hard it bent, and the end he was holding flew up and knocked him down.

Before he could get up again, John shot him.

It was a *very* LONG afternoon.

And then, suddenly, it was very still. And then they all *were* afraid.

Until once more they heard *not* the WAR WHOOP of the wily Iroquois—but the soft sound of the little hoot owl's hoot. Three times they heard it—*towheeeeeheeeee, towheeeeeheeeee, towheeeeeheeeee.* And then three times more—*towheeeeeheeeee, towheeeeeheeeee, towheeeeehee-eee.*

Then it was still again. And they waited. Till far up the ridge, far off, they heard—

"Halloo. Halloo. Anybody left alive at the Dexter cabin?"

John went to the door and flung it wide and called,

"All alive! All alive! All safe at the Dexter cabin."

Then they knew that the men from the fort had come and were pursuing the wily Iroquois.

And that they *were* safe.

So John went out and buried the dead Indians. And he stamped out the burning sparks from the shed, and got more water from the brook and threw it on the charred and smoking logs. He didn't go very far or stay very long because he decided that just then he didn't want to go very far or stay very long.

Anne made birch tea in the blue teapot.

Jim sharpened his new knife.

Sue poked the mud and plaster back in the hole in the wall Jim had made.

Then they all had bread and tea and cold venison—a supper which tasted especially good.

And then because there was still an hour of daylight left, though the shadows were getting longer, they went back to picking up the boulder stones. And working in the garden patch.

But when it grew darker, far off, far far off, so far off it could hardly be heard—they heard, or thought they heard, or almost thought they heard—the WAR WHOOP of the wily Iroquois.

This time, of course, they were mistaken—totally, entirely, utterly, completely, incontrovertibly and most happily MISTAKEN.

Unc' Billy Possum

by THORNTON BURGESS

illustrated by FEODOR ROJANKOVSKY

Reddy Fox had called Unc' Billy Possum a coward. Now
that is a very dreadful thing to call anyone, for no one
respects a coward, and no one likes a coward. But Unc'
Billy Possum had just grinned and then he had dropped
down from the tree beside Reddy Fox and had invited
Reddy to wait for Bowser the Hound, who was coming
down the hill. Reddy didn't know what to do. There was

Bowser in plain sight, and Reddy was afraid, very much afraid. But if he should run before Unc' Billy Possum did, he would prove that he was the coward. And of course, all the little people of the Green Forest and the Green Meadows would know all about it, for Peter Rabbit and Jimmy Skunk had heard Unc' Billy, and at that very minute were watching from safe hiding places.

"Bow, wow, wow!" roared Bowser the Hound in his deepest voice.

Reddy shivered and began to back away; Unc' Billy just grinned. "What makes yo' all's so uneasy?" he asked.

"Bow, wow, wow!" roared Bowser again and began to run straight toward them, with his mouth wide open.

Reddy could stand it no longer. "I—I—I really would like to stay with you, Mr. Possum, but Granny Fox is waiting

for me and I simply cannot stay any longer. Granny wouldn't like it."

Reddy shouted the last words over his shoulder as he started for the Green Meadows at the top of his speed.

"Now who's a coward?" shouted Peter Rabbit and Jimmy Skunk together. Reddy Fox gritted his teeth, but he kept right on running. He didn't even turn to see what became of Unc' Billy Possum.

Now when Reddy started to run Unc' Billy might have climbed a tree, but he didn't. What do you think he did? Why, he just fell over in a heap right in front of Bowser the Hound! Jimmy Skunk almost stopped breathing when he saw him fall, and Peter Rabbit clapped both hands over his eyes as Bowser the Hound stopped by Unc' Billy Possum. He didn't want to see what was going to happen to Unc' Billy.

Bowser the Hound stopped and sniffed at Unc' Billy.

"What's this? What's this?" said Bowser, for he had never seen Unc' Billy Possum before.

Unc' Billy lay there just as if he were dead. Yes, sir, there didn't seem to be any life in Unc' Billy at all. He lay there with his eyes closed and just as limp as a rag. Bowser rolled him over and pulled him this way and pushed him that way, but still Unc' Billy didn't move.

"Huh! Must have frightened him to death," said Bowser. "I'll go on and teach that Reddy Fox a lesson and then I'll come back and take this fellow home to show my master."

So with one more sniff Bowser the Hound started on after Reddy Fox. Peter Rabbit and Jimmy Skunk came out of their hiding places and stood looking down at Unc' Billy.

"Poor Old Uncle Billy," said Peter Rabbit, and shed a few tears.

"Don't drop salt water all over my nice clothes," said a voice as Peter wiped his eyes.

Peter was so startled that he almost knocked Jimmy Skunk over. There lay Unc' Billy grinning at him and slowly winking one eye.

"Did yo' see me fool him?" asked Unc' Billy as he scrambled to his feet. And to this day Bowser the Hound wonders what became of Unc' Billy Possum.

Henry Huggins and Ribs

by BEVERLY CLEARY

illustrated by RICHARD SCARRY

Henry Huggins was in the third grade. His hair looked like a scrubbing brush and most of his grown-up front teeth were in. He lived with his mother and father in a square white house on Klickitat Street. Except for having his tonsils out when he was six and breaking his arm falling out of a cherry tree when he was seven, nothing much happened to Henry.

I wish something exciting would happen, Henry often thought.

But nothing very interesting ever happened to Henry, at least not until one Wednesday afternoon in March. Every Wednesday after school Henry rode downtown on the bus to go swimming at the Y.M.C.A. After he swam for an hour, he got on the bus again and rode home just in time for dinner. It was fun but not really exciting.

When Henry left the Y.M.C.A. on this particular Wednesday, he stopped to watch a man tear down a circus poster. Then, with three nickels and one dime in his pocket, he went to the corner drugstore to buy a chocolate ice cream cone. He thought he would eat the ice cream cone, get on the bus, drop his dime in the slot, and ride home.

This is not what happened.

He bought the ice cream cone and paid for it with one of his nickels. On his way out of the drugstore he stopped to look at funny books. It was a free look, because he had only two nickels left.

He stood there licking his chocolate ice cream cone and reading one of the funny books when he heard a thump, thump, thump. Henry turned, and there behind him was a dog. The dog was scratching himself. He wasn't any special kind of dog. He was too small to be a big dog but, on the other hand, he was much too big to be a little dog. He wasn't a white dog, because parts of him were brown and other parts were black and in between there were yellowish patches. His ears stood up and his tail was long and thin.

The dog was hungry. When Henry licked, he licked. When Henry swallowed, he swallowed.

"Hello, you old dog," Henry said. "You can't have my ice cream cone."

Swish, swish, swish went the tail. "Just one bite," the dog's brown eyes seemed to say.

"Go away," ordered Henry. He wasn't very firm about it. He patted the dog's head.

The tail wagged harder. Henry took one last lick. "Oh, all right," he said. "If you're that hungry, you might as well have it."

The ice cream cone disappeared in one gulp.

"Now go away," Henry told the dog. "I have to catch a bus for home."

He started for the door. The dog started, too.

"Go away, you skinny old dog." Henry didn't say it very

loudly. "Go on home."

The dog sat down at Henry's feet. Henry looked at the dog and the dog looked at Henry.

"I don't think you've got a home. You're awful thin. Your ribs show right through your skin."

Thump, thump, thump replied the tail.

"And you haven't got a collar," said Henry.

He began to think. If only he could keep the dog! He had always wanted a dog of his very own and now he had found a dog that wanted him. He couldn't go home and

127

leave a hungry dog on the street corner. If only he knew what
his mother and father would say! He fingered the two nickels
in his pocket. That was it! He would use one of the nickels
to phone his mother.

"Come on, Ribsy. Come on, Ribs, old boy. I'm going to
call you Ribsy because you're so thin."

The dog trotted after the boy to the telephone booth in
the corner of the drugstore. Henry shoved him into the
booth and shut the door. He had never used a pay telephone
before. He had to put the telephone book on the floor and
stand on tiptoe on it to reach the mouthpiece. He gave the
operator his number and dropped his nickel into the coin
box.

"Hello—Mom?"

"Why, Henry!" His mother sounded surprised. "Where are you?"

"At the drugstore near the Y."

Ribs began to scratch. Thump, thump, thump. Inside the telephone booth the thumps sounded loud and hollow.

"For goodness' sake, Henry, what's that noise?" his mother demanded. Ribs began to whimper and then to howl. "Henry," Mrs. Huggins shouted, "are you all right?"

"Yes, I'm all right," Henry shouted back. He never could understand why his mother always thought something had happened to him when nothing ever did. "That's just Ribsy."

"Ribsy?" His mother was exasperated. "Henry, will you please tell me what is going on?"

"I'm trying to," said Henry. Ribsy howled louder. People were gathering around the phone booth to see what was going on. "Mother, I've found a dog. I sure wish I could keep him. He's a good dog and I'd feed him and wash him and everything. Please, Mom."

"I don't know, dear," his mother said. "You'll have to ask your father."

"Mom!" Henry wailed. "That's what you always say!" Henry was tired of standing on tiptoe and the phone booth was getting warm. "Mom, please say yes and I'll never ask for another thing as long as I live!"

"Well, all right, Henry. I guess there isn't any reason why you shouldn't have a dog. But you'll have to bring him home on the bus. Your father has the car today and I can't come after you. Can you manage?"

"Sure! Easy."

"And Henry, please don't be late. It looks as if it might rain."

"All right, Mom." Thump, thump, thump.

"Henry, what's that thumping noise?"

"It's my dog, Ribsy. He's scratching a flea."

"Oh, Henry," Mrs. Huggins moaned. "Couldn't you have found a dog without fleas?"

Henry thought that was a good time to hang up. "Come on, Ribs," he said. "We're going home on the bus."

When the big green bus stopped in front of the drugstore, Henry picked up his dog. Ribsy was heavier than he expected. He had a hard time getting him into the bus and was wondering how he would get a dime out of his pocket when the driver said, "Say, sonny, you can't take that dog on the bus."

"Why not?" asked Henry.

"It's a company rule, sonny. No dogs on buses."

"Golly, Mister, how'm I going to get him home? I just

have to get him home."

"Sorry, sonny. I didn't make the rule. No animal can ride on a bus unless it's inside a box."

"Well, thanks anyway," said Henry doubtfully, and lifted Ribsy off the bus.

"Well, I guess we'll have to get a box. I'll get you onto the next bus somehow," promised Henry.

He went back into the drugstore followed closely by Ribsy. "Have you got a big box I could have, please?" he asked the man at the toothpaste counter. "I need one big enough for my dog."

The clerk leaned over the counter to look at Ribsy. "A cardboard box?" he asked.

"Yes, please," said Henry, wishing the man would hurry. He didn't want to be late getting home.

The clerk pulled a box out from under the counter. "This hair tonic carton is the only one I have. I guess it's big enough, but why anyone would want to put a dog in a cardboard box I can't understand."

The box was about two feet square and six inches deep. On one end was printed, "Don't Let Them Call You Baldy," and on the other, "Try Our Large Economy Size."

Henry thanked the clerk, carried the box out to the bus stop, and put it on the sidewalk. Ribsy padded after him. "Get in, fellow," Henry commanded. Ribsy understood. He stepped into the box and sat down just as the bus came around the corner. Henry had to kneel to pick up the box. It was not a very strong box and he had to put his arms under it. He staggered as he lifted it, feeling like the strong man who lifted weights at the circus. Ribsy lovingly licked his face with his wet pink tongue.

"Hey, cut that out!" Henry ordered. "You better be good if you're going to ride on the bus with me."

The bus stopped at the curb. When it was Henry's turn to get on, he had trouble finding the step because he couldn't see his feet. He had to try several times before he hit it. Then he discovered he had forgotten to take his dime out of his pocket. He was afraid to put the box down for fear Ribsy might escape.

He turned sideways to the driver and asked politely, "Will you please take the dime out of my pocket for me? My hands are full."

The driver pushed his cap back on his head and exclaimed, "Full! I should say they *are* full! And just where do you think you're going with that animal?"

"Home," said Henry in a small voice.

The passengers were staring and most of them were smiling. The box was getting heavier every minute

"Not on this bus, you're not!" said the driver.

"But the man on the last bus said I could take the dog on the bus in a box," protested Henry, who was afraid he couldn't hold the dog much longer. "He said it was a company rule."

"He meant a big box tied shut. A box with holes punched in it for the dog to breathe through."

Henry was horrified to hear Ribsy growl. "Shut up," he ordered.

Ribsy began to scratch his left ear with his left hind foot. The box began to tear. Ribsy jumped out of the box and off the bus and Henry jumped after him. The bus pulled away with a puff of exhaust.

"Now see what you've done! You've spoiled everything." The dog hung his head and tucked his tail between his legs. "If I can't get you home, how can I keep you?"

Henry sat down on the curb to think. It was so late and the clouds were so dark that he didn't want to waste time looking for a big box. His mother was probably beginning to worry about him.

People were stopping on the corner to wait for the next bus. Among them Henry noticed an elderly lady carrying a large paper shopping bag full of apples. The shopping bag gave him an idea. Jumping up, he snapped his fingers at Ribs and ran back into the drugstore.

"You back again?" asked the toothpaste clerk. "What do you want this time? String and paper to wrap your dog in?"

"No, sir," said Henry. "I want one of those big nickel shopping bags." He laid his last nickel on the counter.

"Well, I'll be darned," said the clerk, and handed the bag across the counter.

Henry opened the bag and set it up on the floor. He picked up Ribsy and shoved him hind feet first into the bag. Then he pushed his front feet in. A lot of Ribsy was left over.

The clerk was leaning over the counter watching. "I guess I'll have to have some string and paper, too," Henry said, "if I can have some free."

"Well! Now I've seen everything." The clerk shook his head as he handed a piece of string and a big sheet of paper across the counter.

Ribsy whimpered, but he held still while Henry wrapped the paper loosely around his head and shoulders and tied

it with the string. The dog made a lumpy package, but by taking one handle of the bag in each hand Henry was able to carry it to the bus stop. He didn't think the bus driver would notice him. It was getting dark and a crowd of people, most of them with packages, was waiting on the corner. A few spatters of rain hit the pavement.

This time Henry remembered his dime. Both hands were full, so he held the dime in his teeth and stood behind the woman with the bag of apples. Ribsy wiggled and whined, even though Henry tried to pet him through the paper. When the bus stopped, he climbed on behind the lady, quickly set the bag down, dropped his dime in the slot, picked up the bag, and squirmed through the crowd to a seat beside a fat man near the back of the bus.

"Whew!" Henry sighed with relief. The driver was the same one he had met on the first bus! But Ribs was on the bus at last. Now if he could only keep him quiet for fifteen minutes they would be home and Ribsy would be his for keeps.

The next time the bus stopped Henry saw Scooter Mc-Carthy, a fifth grader at school, get on and make his way through the crowd to the back of the bus.

Just my luck, thought Henry. I'll bet he wants to know what's in my bag.

"Hi," said Scooter.

"Hi," said Henry.

"Whatcha got in that bag?" asked Scooter.

"None of your beeswax," answered Henry.

Scooter looked at Henry. Henry looked at Scooter. Crackle, crackle, crackle went the bag. Henry tried to hold it more tightly between his knees.

"There's something alive in that bag!" Scooter said accusingly.

"Shut up, Scooter!" whispered Henry.

"Aw, shut up yourself!" said Scooter. "You've got something alive in that bag!"

By this time the passengers at the back of the bus were staring at Henry and his package. Crackle, crackle, crackle. Henry tried to pat Ribsy again through the paper. The bag crackled even louder. Then it began to wiggle.

"Come on, tell us what's in the bag," coaxed the fat man.

"N-n-n-nothing," stammered Henry. "Just something I found."

"Maybe it's a rabbit," suggested one passenger. "I think

136

it's kicking."

"No, it's too big for a rabbit," said another.

"I'll bet it's a baby," said Scooter. "I'll bet you kidnaped a baby!"

"I did not!"

Ribs began to whimper and then to howl. Crackle, crackle, crackle. Thump, thump, thump. Ribsy scratched his way out of the bag.

"Well, I'll be doggoned!" exclaimed the fat man and began to laugh. "I'll be doggoned!"

"It's just a skinny old dog," said Scooter.

"He is not! He's a good dog."

Henry tried to keep Ribsy between his knees. The bus lurched around a corner and started to go uphill. Henry was thrown against the fat man. The frightened dog wiggled away from him, squirmed between the passengers, and started for the front of the bus.

"Here, Ribsy, old boy! Come back here," called Henry and started after him.

"E-e-ek! A dog!" squealed the lady with the bag of apples. "Go away, doggie, go away!"

Ribsy was scared. He tried to run and crashed into the lady's bag of apples. The bag tipped over and the apples began to roll toward the back of the bus, which was grinding up a steep hill. The apples rolled around the feet of the people who were standing. Passengers began to slip and slide. They dropped their packages and grabbed one another.

Crash! A high-school girl dropped an armload of books.

Rattle! Bang! Crash! A lady dropped a big paper bag. The bag broke open and pots and pans rolled out.

Thud! A man dropped a coil of garden hose. The hose unrolled and the passengers found it wound around their legs.

People were sitting on the floor. They were sitting on books and apples. They were even sitting on other people's laps. Some of them had their hats over their faces and their feet in the air.

Skree-e-etch! The driver threw on the brakes and turned around in his seat just as Henry made his way through the apples and books and pans and hose to catch Ribsy.

The driver pushed his cap back on his head. "O.K., sonny," he said to Henry. "Now you know why dogs aren't allowed on busses!"

"Yes, sir," said Henry in a small voice. "I'm sorry."

"You're sorry! A lot of good that does. Look at this bus! Look at those people!"

"I didn't mean to make any trouble," said Henry. "My mother said I could keep the dog if I could bring him home on the bus."

The fat man began to snicker. Then he chuckled. Then he laughed and then he roared. He laughed until tears streamed down his cheeks and all the other passengers were laughing too, even the man with the hose and the lady with the apples.

The driver didn't laugh. "Take that dog and get off the bus!" he ordered. Ribsy whimpered and tucked his tail between his legs.

The fat man stopped laughing. "See here, driver," he said, "you can't put that boy and his dog off in the rain."

"Well, he can't stay on the bus," snapped the driver.

Henry didn't know what he was going to do. He guessed he'd have to walk the rest of the way home. He wasn't sure he knew the way in the dark.

Just then a siren screamed. It grew louder and louder until it stopped right alongside the bus.

A policeman appeared in the entrance. "Is there a boy called Henry Huggins on this bus?" he asked.

"Oh boy, you're going to be arrested for having a dog on the bus!" gloated Scooter. "I'll bet you have to go to jail!"

"I'm him," said Henry in a very small voice.

"I am he," corrected the lady with the apples, who had been a schoolteacher and couldn't help correcting boys.

"You'd better come along with us," said the policeman.

"Boy, you're sure going to get it!" said Scooter.

"Surely going to get it," corrected the apple lady.

Henry and Ribsy followed the policeman off the bus and into the squad car, where Henry and the dog sat in the back seat.

"Are you going to arrest me?" Henry asked timidly.

"Well, I don't know. Do you think you ought to be arrested?"

"No, sir," said Henry politely. He thought the policeman was joking, but he wasn't sure. It was hard to tell about grownups sometimes. "I didn't mean to do anything. I just had to get Ribsy home.My mother said I could keep him if I could bring him home on the bus."

"What do you think?" the officer asked his partner, who was driving the squad car.

"We-e-ell, I think we might let him off this time," answered the driver. "His mother must be pretty worried about him if she called the police, and I don't think she'd want him to go to jail."

"Yes, he's late for his dinner already. Let's see how fast we can get him home."

The driver pushed a button and the siren began to shriek. Ribsy raised his head and howled. The tires sucked at the wet pavement and the windshield wipers splip-splopped. Henry began to enjoy himself. Wouldn't this be something to tell the kids at school! Automobiles pulled over to the curb as the police car went faster and faster. Even the bus Henry had been on had to pull over and stop. Henry waved to the passengers. They waved back. Up the hill the police car sped and around the corner until they came to Klickitat Street and then to Henry's block and then pulled up in front of his house.

Henry's mother and father were standing on the porch waiting for him. The neighbors were looking out of their windows.

"Well!" said his father after the policemen had gone. "It's about time you came home. So this is Ribsy! I've heard about you, fellow, and there's a big bone and a can of Feeley's Flea Flakes waiting for you."

"Henry, what *will* you do next?" sighed his mother.

"Golly, Mom, I didn't do anything. I just brought my dog home on the bus like you said."

Ribsy sat down and began to scratch.

The Baker's Daughter

by MARGERY WILLIAMS BIANCO

illustrated by LAWRENCE BEALL SMITH

O but the Baker's Daughter is beautiful!

The Baker's Daughter has yellow hair, and every night it is curled with rags, and every morning it stands out in a frizzy fluff round her head. The Baker's Daughter has blue dresses and pink dresses and spotted dresses, with flounces and flounces on them; she has beads around her neck and jingly bracelets and a ring with a real stone. All the girls in class sigh with envy of the Baker's Daughter.

But the Baker's Daughter is proud. She points her chin and she turns up her nose, and she is very, very superior. You never see her in the Baker's shop. She strolls up and down the sidewalk, sucking her beads.

You all know the Baker's shop, two steps down. It is warm in there, and busy. It smells of hot bread, and every few minutes the Baker, a hot, untidy little man in shirt sleeves, comes up from the basement carrying a big tray of crullers, or shiny rolls, or twisted currant buns. The Baker works hard all day and he never has time to do more than just poke his nose outside the doorway, every hour or so, for a sniff of cool air. It is hard to believe that anything so beautiful as the Baker's Daughter could ever come out of the Baker's shop!

Once I started to write a poem. It began:

> *O it is the Baker's Daughter,*
> *And she is grown so fair, so fair . . .*

I thought I would make a very splendid valentine of it, all written out in a fine hand, with pink roses around and lots of crinkly paper lace, and send it to her, secretly. But unfortunately I found out that it was too much like a poem that someone else wrote a long time ago, and so I have never finished it. But still it always comes into my mind whenever I see the Baker's Daughter sucking her beads.

There was only one thing in the Baker's shop that at all

came up in magnificence to the Baker's Daughter herself, and that was the big round cake that sat in the place of honor, right in the middle of the Baker's window. It was a chocolate cake, with all sorts of twirls and twiddles of lovely icing on it, and the word B I R T H D A Y written in pink sugar letters. For some reason or other the Baker would never sell that cake. Perhaps he was afraid he would never be able to make another one quite so beautiful. He would sell you any other cake from his window but that one, and even if you went there very early of a Friday morning, which is cruller day, when there are no cakes at all, and asked him for a nice party cake, he would say:

"I can let you have one by three o'clock!"

And if you then asked: "But how about the cake in the window?" he would reply:

"That's not for sale. You can have one by three o'clock!"

For though you should offer him dollars and dollars, he would never sell that cake!

I seldom dare to speak to the Baker's Daughter. I am much too humble. But still she has friends. Never little boys; these she points her chin at, from across the street. But there are little girls with whom she is on friendly terms for as much as a week at a time. Naturally they are very proud. If you can't be a princess or a movie star perhaps the next best thing is to be seen walking up to the drug store soda

fountain with the Baker's Daughter, and sitting there beside her on a tall stool eating pineapple sundae.

Now there was one little girl with whom the Baker's Daughter condescended at one time to be friends. Perhaps her name had something to do with it. She was called Carmelita Miggs, and Carmelita is a very romantic and superior name. She had black hair and a pair of bronze slippers, and she was the only little girl ever seen to stroll

publicly with the Baker's Daughter, arm in arm. What they talked about no one knew. But Carmelita sometimes wore the Baker's Daughter's beads, and the Baker's Daughter would wear Carmelita's beads, and altogether they were very, very special friends while it lasted.

And it lasted until Carmelita had a birthday party.

The Baker's Daughter of course was invited, and several other of Carmelita's school friends. It was to be a real party, at four in the afternoon, with ice cream. And the Baker's Daughter said, very grandly, that she would bring a cake.

"I will bake you a nice one," said her father, "with orange icing on it. Now let me see . . . how many of you will there be?"

But that wasn't at all what the Baker's Daughter wanted. Anyone at all could bring a cake with orange icing. "I will choose my own cake!" thought the Baker's Daughter.

But all she said was: "That will be very nice!"

And in the afternoon, while her father was down in the bake-shop kitchen putting the last twiddle on the orange cake (for he wanted to make it something very special), and while her mother was taking forty winks in the back parlor, and the bakery cat was sound asleep, with her four paws curled under her, behind the counter, the Baker's Daughter crept into the shop on tiptoe, in all her finery, and stole—yes, *stole*—that big magnificent cake from the very middle of the shop window!

You see, she had had her eye on it, all along!

She lifted it up—and a nice, light cake it seemed—wooden platter and all, and she covered it over with sheets of waxy paper and carried it round to Carmelita's house.

O but she looked proud, walking down the street with that big cake in her arms! Everyone turned to look at her.

"What a lovely cake!" cried all the little boys and girls when she arrived at Carmelita's house.

And the wrappings were taken off, very carefully, and it was set right in the middle of the table, with candles all around it.

"*What* a nice light cake!" said Carmelita's mother.

"All good cakes are light!" said the Baker's Daughter.

"It was very, very kind of your father to make such a splendid cake," said Carmelita's mother.

"I chose it myself!" said the Baker's Daughter, tossing her head.

They talked a little, very politely, and Carmelita Miggs showed all her birthday presents. And at last came the moment for the ice cream to be handed round on little glass plates.

"And now," said Carmelita's mother, "we'll all have some of that delicious cake!"

Carmelita had to cut it, because it was her birthday. She stood there feeling very shy, for there was a great silence all round; everyone's eyes were fixed on the cake, and all one could hear was Tommy Bates busily sucking his ice-cream spoon, so as to get through first.

Only the Baker's Daughter sat there proudly, with her skirts spread out, looking indifferent, as though cakes like this were quite an everyday affair with her!

Carmelita took the knife and stuck it into the very middle of the pink icing, and pushed. You could have heard a pin drop.

But the knife didn't go in. Carmelita turned very red, and took a long breath and tried again.

Still the knife wouldn't go in.

"You must try harder, dear," said Carmelita's mother, smiling pleasantly. "I expect the top icing is a little bit stiff! Do you want me to help you?"

Now Carmelita knew that she had been pushing just as hard as she could. It came upon her, all at once, that there

151

must be something very very queer about that cake! But she took another long breath, again, and this time her mother put *her* hand on the knife, too.

You could have heard *two* pins drop!

And then, suddenly, there was a funny "plop," and the knife went in. And as it went in the cake slipped and turned a sort of somersault, and there it was, upside down, sticking on the tip of the knife that Carmelita's mother was still holding, and everyone looking most surprised. And that

wasn't the worst of it!

It was all hollow inside!

In fact, it was just a big pasteboard shell covered over with icing, and *that* was why the Baker would never sell it to anyone!

Can you imagine how the party felt? How the little boys and girls whispered and giggled, how Carmelita wept and the Baker's Daughter grew redder and redder, and snifflier and snifflier, and how Carmelita's mother tried to smooth everything over and pretend that it was really all very funny, and quite the nicest thing that could happen at any birthday party? And how, at the very last minute, while the ice cream was all melting away, they had to send out and buy a real cake, *somewhere else!*

But Carmelita Miggs didn't think it was a joke. She never, never forgave the Baker's Daughter for spoiling her party. For quite a long time she wouldn't speak to her at all. As for the other boys and girls, whenever they met Carmelita or the Baker's Daughter they would say:

"Now we'll all have some cake!"

You would think, after this, that the Baker's Daughter would have changed her ways. But not a bit of it! I saw her, only the other day, strolling up and down the sidewalk and sucking her beads just as proud as ever.

As I went past her I whispered very softly: "Now we'll all have some cake!"

And do you know what the Baker's Daughter did? I hate to tell you.

She stuck—out—her—her—tongue!

There, in the middle of the Baker's window, is another cake. This time it has green icing and pink roses, and two little sugar doves on top. It is even grander than the old one, and will probably last twice as long.

Unless, of course, someone else should have a birthday party!

Let's Go to Portugal

Portugal is in the southwestern corner of Europe where it shares the Iberian Peninsula with the larger country of Spain. Spain and the Atlantic Ocean, which lies at Portugal's doorstep, have been major influences in her history. Over the centuries, Spain made many attempts to conquer her smaller neighbor; sometimes she succeeded.

Early Portugal was ruled by the Goths, Romans, Moors, and Spaniards. The beginnings of Portugal as a kingdom independent from Spain go back to the twelfth century. Portugal's Prince Henry the Navigator, exploring the sea for a new route to India, helped to create a vast Portuguese empire by the mid-sixteenth century. The country became one of the world's richest nations and a great sea power. Later wars and invasions lost her some of her far-flung colonies, like Brazil. Yet today tiny Portugal still possesses an empire nearly one-third as large as the United States!

Portugal is a republic now, run by a president, premier, and a one-house legislature. The country's mountainous north provides fine wine vineyards and pastures for livestock. There are rich groves of cork and olive trees in the central sections, while the dry south yields nuts and citrus fruit. Along the seacoast, fishermen bring in tuna, sardines, and a variety of fish for canning and export. The Portuguese people love music and dancing. Like the Spaniards, they enjoy bullfights, but they do not kill the bulls. Home handicrafts, mining, and the tourist trade are improving Portugal's economic development.

Portugal's most popular shrine, Our Lady of Fatima

The busy harbor of Lisbon, capital of Portugal

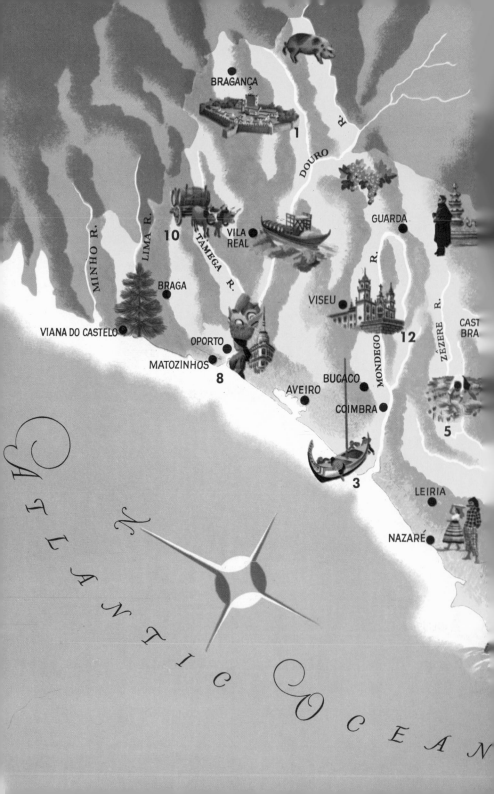

BRAGANÇA

1

DOURO R.

GUARDA

10

VILA REAL

TÂMEGA R.

MINHO R.

LIMA R.

BRAGA

VIANA DO CASTELO

OPORTO

MATOZINHOS

8

VISEU

MONDEGO R.

ZÊZERE R.

CAST BRA

12

AVEIRO

BUCACO

COIMBRA

5

3

LEIRIA

NAZARÉ

ATLANTIC OCEAN

Can you find the following things on this map? **1.** Braganca, walled city **2.** Woman taking pottery to market **3.** Colorful fishing boats and fishermen **4.** Stripping cork **5.** Farmer harvesting rice **6.** Orange tree **7.** Migratory ducks flying south **8.** Woman carrying hats to market **9.** Folk dancing **10.** Ox-drawn carts transporting wine casks **11.** Swimming at Portugal's fine bathing beaches **12.** Misericordia Cathedral **13.** Fisherman, in traditional tasseled hat and plaid trousers, casting his net **14.** A bullfight

S P A I N

PORTALEGRE

2

GUADIANA R.

4

ÉVORA

7

BEJA

9

ESTREMADURA

NTARÉM 14

SADO R.

SETÚBAL

LISBON

CINTRA

ESTORIL

1

ALGARVE

6 FARO

13

CAPE ST. VINCENT

Portugal's coat of arms   A young girl learns to spin.

Nazaré, a colorful fishing village on the Atlantic